DANCING CLOUD

DANCING CLOUD

The Navajo Boy

By Mary Marsh Buff, with lithographs by Conrad Buff

1890-

NEW YORK · THE VIKING PRESS · MCMXLV

FIRST PUBLISHED MARCH 1937
SECOND PRINTING SEPTEMBER 1938
THIRD PRINTING MARCH 1945
FOURTH PRINTING MARCH 1950

CONTENTS

Navajo	7	Watering Day and a Rabbit	41
Building the Hogan	9	Planting Corn	47
The Dawn People	13	The Great Cloudburst	51
Uncle Tells a Story	18	Spring Shearing	59
Wildhorse	25	Eagles and Turquoise	68
Dancing Cloud's Mother	33	Trading Post	

ILLUSTRATIONS

COLOR

Navajo Country	6	Happy Girl	53
Wildhorse Coiled His Rope	29	The Great Cloudburst	56
Dancing Cloud's Mother	39	Dancing Cloud	67
Watering Day	42	The Silversmith	74

BLACK AND WHITE

Dancing Cloud's Home	8	She Began to Play with the Puppies	35
The High Red Cliffs	12	Planting Corn	49
Uncle Tells a Story	23	Sheep Shearing	61
Searching for Water	26	Carding and Spinning	64
Home from the Trading Post	79		

NAVAJO

IN a far-off Arizona desert lives a proud, handsome tribe of Indians, the Navajo. Navajo is an old word for "cultivated fields."

Once the Navajo Indians were fierce and warlike. When riding their thin, desert horses, they were greatly feared by the peaceful village Indians. That was a long time ago.

The Navajo Indians, now, are herders of great flocks of sheep and goats. Navajo herds wander over the wide sagebrush country, between red rocks and dark cedar trees, searching for grass in a country of little rain. Their herds and their fields of corn have made the Navajo a peaceful people.

BUILDING THE HOGAN

CLOSE to the foot of the high red cliffs of Pottery Butte is a Navajo hogan, a log and mud home like a brown beehive. In it live Dancing Cloud and Lost Tooth, two Navajo children. Although the children have other hogans to live in when they drive their sheep to far-away pastures, this one is the winter hogan, their real home.

Dancing Cloud and Lost Tooth had both helped build this hogan.

The boy and the father, Wildhorse, harnessed two horses to the old green wagon one morning and drove to Cedar Ridge. There grew many cedar trees. All day long they cut trees into logs. Late that afternoon the horses pulled the heavy load back to Pottery Butte.

[9]

Many friends came the next morning to help with the building of the hogan. It had six sides. Logs were notched and stacked until the walls were as high as the shoulders of a tall man. Then the men began the roof, putting shorter logs close together. The roof grew round.

As they neared the peak of the roof, Dancing Cloud called to his father high on the roof: "Make the smoke hole large enough so smoke will not get into our eyes."

"But if it is too large, little brother, rain and snow will come in," answered his father.

Swift Boy, a friend of Dancing Cloud, had a stove in his hogan with a stovepipe. The long pipe took out the smoke into the air. Wildhorse said that if there were no smoke hole the tchindi, the evil spirits, could not get out of the hogan. They would stay inside and make the family sick.

Between the logs were many holes. Lost Tooth and the visiting children mixed red clay with water and filled the holes with mud, small twigs, and cedar bark. Then the walls were solid and tight against rain and wind.

The children's mother, The Weaver, was cooking.

In the shade of the shelter of cedar trees, called the summer house, the women were watching boiling mutton, stirring corn mush, and preparing coffee.

"The hogan is finished," called Wildhorse.

All the friends gathered around the new building. Wildhorse took from his buckskin bag a handful of sacred corn meal. He entered the house and rubbed it on the logs that held the walls. He made a circle of meal inside the hogan. Then he chanted in a soft voice, while all listened:

"May the house be blessed,
From my head to my feet,
Where I lie and all above me,
All around me may it be holy."

As in all Navajo hogans, the doorway faced the rising sun.

Lost Tooth brought an old blanket to her father. "Father, here is the door."

He fastened the thick old blanket to the frame.

The time of feasting had come. The Weaver entered the house and built a fire. To make the fire happy, she fed it with food. In came steaming mutton, boiling coffee, and hot mush. In came the friends. The Pottery Butte hogan was finished.

THE DAWN PEOPLE

SCATTERED everywhere about Pottery Butte, the children found broken pieces of decorated pottery. Dancing Cloud asked his father: "Where does this pottery come from? It is all over the ground."

Wildhorse looked up at the high red cliffs that towered above him and answered: "The Dawn People made this pottery. They once lived on the top of the high hill which is the butte. It is said they had a secret trail up there, but no one has ever found it."

This was the first time Dancing Cloud had heard of the Dawn People. He wondered what the top of the butte where they once lived looked like. He wondered where the secret trail began, or if the Dawn People had destroyed it when they went away.

[13]

For several days the children searched for the trail. But on all sides of the butte, walls of rock went straight up into the blue sky. "The Dawn People were safe up there," said Dancing Cloud.

"But they had to come down sometimes for water," said his sister.

One afternoon Lost Tooth saw a cliff swallow flutter out of a nest hidden in a crack in the cliff.

"I will climb up there," she called to her brother, "and see if there are any eggs in the nest."

Her moccasined feet found small footholds in the rocks. When she reached the nest, she called down: "Big Brother, I see a trail all the way up this crack in the cliff to the very top. Come up and see. We have found the old trail!"

Excitedly he joined her, and the two children climbed upward. The trail was worn and old. Loose rocks had fallen across it since the time of the Dawn People. The children had to be careful not to slip. They caught hold of small shrubs that grew between the cracks in the rock. More than once they thought they could go no higher. Then the girl, who was above her brother, called: "We are here."

The children stood on the top of Pottery Butte. It stretched flat before them. Not a tree or a bush grew upon it. Nothing but barren rock. Here and there a few piles of rock, heaped as though by men, broke the flatness of the great floor.

"How far we can see!" cried the children when they had caught their breath. To the southeast they could just see a pine-covered mountain where their uncle, Many Goats, hunted for deer. To the north lay the dark-blue bulk of Navajo Mountain, sacred to the Navajo.

"Look," called Dancing Cloud. "There is Swift Boy's hogan. Those little white spots are his sheep. I see the well at Sweetwater Wash, and you know how far away that is."

"I see the green trees at the trading post," answered Lost Tooth.

Dancing Cloud stepped to the edge of the butte and looked down. "See the hogan, how small it is; and Long Ears looks like the clay toy you made of him," said Dancing Cloud laughing.

"Don't go so close, a rock might slip," warned Lost Tooth, and she pulled him from the edge.

After the children grew tired of looking, they began to explore the flat top of the butte. Dancing Cloud found a pointed stick. He dug in a pile of heaped-up rocks. All was quiet up there on the top of the world so close to the deep sky. Only far-off sheep bells and cries of frightened birds came gently to their ears.

Suddenly Dancing Cloud called to his sister: "See what I have found," and he held up a little flat bowl with red figures painted upon it. "It isn't broken."

Lost Tooth called back to him: "I have found corn and a piece of brown cloth," and she ran to him smiling. Lost Tooth had found a piece of cloth that once was a part of a sandal which belonged to one of the Dawn People. From her uncle, Many Goats, Lost Tooth had heard that before the Spaniards brought sheep to the Navajo, the Indians had woven with plant fibers and cotton.

The children, interested in their discoveries, had not noticed the sun going down behind a distant mesa. The top of the high cliff was still glowing in the early evening light when the near-by sound of sheep bells and the barking of dogs made them look up. Wildhorse must be bringing in the flock.

"I will leave the bowl here," said Dancing Cloud. "I cannot carry it down the steep trail without breaking it. We know the way now, we can come back."

The two children began to go down the trail. Dancing Cloud went first. In the fading light he had to be very careful. The trail was as hard to climb down as to climb up. They both slipped more than once.

When they reached the ground, Wildhorse had just driven the sheep into the corral built around a cave in the cliff. They ran up to him.

"Father, we have found the secret way to the top of the butte. We climbed up there. We found things in the rocks."

"What things?"—and the father's face clouded.

"A little bowl and corn and cloth," answered Dancing Cloud. "We left them there. The trail is steep."

"Children," said Wildhorse, and his face was strange to them, "never touch anything of the Dawn People. Tchindi, the evil spirits of the dead, live in them." The fear in his voice made the children quiet and afraid of they knew not what. Quietly they went into the cheer of the evening hogan.

UNCLE TELLS A STORY

A COLD north wind swept down on Navajo Land. Dancing Cloud drove his flock of sheep and goats toward the new Pottery Butte home. He counted his lambs and found that one was missing. The missing lamb was the black one with brown streaks. The boy had seen it only a short time before among the rocks of Twin Buttes.

Dancing Cloud stopped. He listened. The wind howled. Then he listened again. The wind changed, and he heard a far-off bleat, sad and faint. Telling the dogs to stay with the flock, he quickly walked toward the sound. It became louder, bleat, bleat, bleat. Was a coyote after his baby lamb? In fear he ran fast toward the sound. There was the lamb, caught between two rocks. It pushed itself forward and wedged itself tighter. If it had only pushed back it would have been free. Lambs are little fools.

With gentle hands, Dancing Cloud lifted the lamb from between the rocks. It gave him a "Thank you" bleat, and meekly followed him back to the flock, quite unhurt.

Swinging his tin can filled with stones, Dancing Cloud urged the sheep on. It was cold and getting late. The sun had already hidden itself behind Twin Buttes when the Navajo boy let down the bars of the corral. In crowded the cold and weary sheep, back into the warm cave Wildhorse used as a barn. Dancing Cloud carefully put back the bars and started for the hogan.

But Black Nose, his puppy, jumped and whined as he walked. Black Nose wanted to go into the hogan, where it was warm, and get a mutton bone to chew. Dogs were not allowed in the hogan, but Dancing Cloud picked up his puppy and hid it under his coat. He pushed aside the curtain door. Supper smells made his nose happy. The new hogan was cozy and warm, and he was hungry. He threw himself down on the soft pile of sheepskins. His mother was cooking over the fire in the center of the room. Wildhorse was making a pair of moccasins. Lost Tooth was playing with her kittens and a ball of red yarn. Baby brother slept quietly in his cradleboard.

The flickering fire sent a bright ray into a dark corner. Dancing Cloud caught sight of his uncle's smiling face. He loved his uncle, Many Goats. Many Goats never forgot the children. Every time he came to visit them, oranges or candies were hidden in the pockets of his blue jeans. He brought venison back every fall when he went to the mountains hunting for deer. Best of all, he told stories of the great deeds of the Navajo; of battles, raids, and captives taken from enemy villages. Uncle would tell them a story tonight after eating.

The Navajo mother, making squawbread, mixed flour, water, and baking powder together. From the sticky dough, her brown hands patted out little flat cakes. She dipped each into a pot of sizzling mutton fat. Pop, pop, the grease sputtered out of the kettle in hot drops. A baby kitten, the white one, scampered a little too near. A drop of fat lit right on his little black nose. Lost Tooth laughed as the kitten scampered back to her and her ball of yarn.

"Now we can eat," called the mother. Mutton stew, squawbread, brown and bumpy, black coffee, and goat's milk from Lost Tooth's own goat.

Black Nose, the puppy, began to squirm under Dancing Cloud's sheepskin. The boy kept him quiet by giving him a piece of mutton bone to chew. The rest of the family did not notice, busy with their own noisy talk.

[20]

"Uncle brought us peaches from the trading post," the mother said, as they finished their stew.

Peaches were a treat. Dancing Cloud on his warm sheepskin was happy and comfortable. Forgotten was the long day, the biting wind; forgotten, too, the lost lamb that was found again.

"Uncle," begged Dancing Cloud, when the meal was over, "tell us a story tonight. About Kit Carson, the Rope Thrower, and the canyon, and Navajo battles with white soldiers."

"Yes," smiled his uncle, "I have told it to you many times. I will tell it to you again." And this is the story the uncle told:

"Our people have always called themselves The Dineh, which means The People. We are The People. The Spaniards called us Navajo, but that is not our real name. The People lived in a great canyon five days' journey to the northeast of where we now live. It is called now the canyon de Chelly. Red cliffs rise straight up into the sky on all sides. Enemies can enter the canyon at only one or two places. The Dineh were safe within the rocky walls.

"In rich bottom lands of the canyon, where water flowed, The Dineh grew squash and melons, and raised fine peaches. With hoes which were made of the shoulder blades of antelopes, we cultivated bright Indian corn. Sheep grew fat. Captured women from enemy villages taught our women to weave fine blankets from the wool of our sheep. So fine were they, no water could go through them. The Dineh grew great and prospered.

"Many years passed. From Spaniards we got horses. Then evil days fell upon us. The Utes, the Mexicans, and even our old blood brothers, the Apaches, made war upon us. Cattle, sheep, and horses were stolen from us. Corn fields were laid waste. Many young warriors were killed.

"At last there came a day when the Great White Chief in Washington sent soldiers to capture The Dineh. Their leader was Rope Thrower. White men called him Kit Carson. Rope Thrower led his men into the canyon. The white men had guns. They had cannon that spit fire. They burned our fields. They drove away our sheep and horses. They burned our peach trees and our hogans. We had no wood to keep us warm. We ate the bodies of our dead horses. We starved. At last they captured us.

"The white men took us from our land. They made us walk many days, three hundred miles east to Hwalte in New Mexico. The sick and old rode in ox carts. The Dineh have always called the journey The Big Walk.

"Five years we lived in New Mexico. They were evil years. We planted corn. Worms ate it all. There was little wood. We were cold. Many of us sickened and died. We grew sad for our old land. We asked to go back to it.

"But the Great White Father at Washington wished to send us to Oklahoma, where the land was good. He said we could grow tall corn there. We did not want to go to Oklahoma. We longed only for the country of our forefathers.

"So homesick were we, and so unhappy, that we asked only for the land of our fathers and an old buck goat. We told the white men we would tie the old buck goat by his horns to a tree. All our young men who passed by would see that he would butt his head against the tree until he died. He could fight no longer. We, too, could fight no longer.

"The Great White Father felt for us. He let us return to the land of our fathers. To each of us he gave blankets, food, and two sheep."

Dancing Cloud stared into the fire. He was one of The Dineh, The People. In the ancient Dineh Land, which stretched miles north, south, east, and west from where he sat staring into the fire, The Dineh have lived, peaceful and happy, since the day of their return.

WILDHORSE

MANY years ago, when Dancing Cloud's father was a young man, there came a summer so dry and hot that it was long remembered by all the Indians. Even Blind Jo, the oldest Navajo, told Dancing Cloud there never had been such a dry summer in all of his ninety years.

Springs where sheep and horses had found water even in the hottest months dried up entirely. Then it was that the Navajo went out from the borders of Navajo Land. In their creaking old wagons, loaded with water barrels, they explored unknown canyons, looking for water. They dug deep holes in sandy creek beds, hoping water might seep up from below.

Sheep, cattle, and horses died of thirst. Usually in August sudden torrents of rain poured down on the thirsty earth. But for some strange reason, this sad summer the skies were always a deep blue.

One August morning during that fateful summer, Wildhorse saddled his horse before sunrise. An Indian told him there was a spring in a far-distant part of Navajo Land, called Box Spring. He said that it often flowed even in the very driest years. But it was so far away, and so high up in the mountains, that many Indians did not go there.

Tugging along slowly in deep sand, Wildhorse headed his animal toward the rising sun. The dark walls gradually crept higher on each side of the creek bed. They finally blocked out most of the deep blue of the summer sky.

After many hours of slow plodding through deep sand, the Indian saw a very high red cliff before him. It stopped the canyon just like the side of a box. No man or beast could climb that steep cliff. Here must be Box Spring.

As he came around a bend in the trail, his tired horse lifted his head and whinnied. The rider looked up. To his surprise, playing in the cool, deep shadows of the canyon, he saw a small band of horses. A pure white stallion, large and beautiful, was leading them.

The Indian had happened upon a band of wild horses. Here was good fortune. Only a summer dry and hot could have driven these untamed horses down from their high mesa homes to this cool canyon to hunt for water. The Indian had found not only water, but horses.

Although Wildhorse and The Weaver had a large flock of sheep and goats, they had but two horses. They needed more. If Wildhorse could rope the leader, it would be easier to catch the others. No horse could climb the cliff behind them. They could only get away through the narrow entrance of the canyon where the Indian stood.

Wildhorse took from his saddle the extra blanket he always carried. He hung it in the narrow entrance of the canyon. Wild horses will run over a man, if need be, to get away from him, but the blanket, hanging across the entrance, would seem to the horses like a solid gate. They would not come near it.

When the horses smelled and saw the Indian, they raced around the little canyon like mad. Wildhorse quickly pulled his rope from the saddle horn and coiled it. Whiz, it went through the air. Neatly it circled the white neck of the beautiful stallion. With swift hands, the Navajo tied the other end

around a sturdy tree. The animal kicked and whinnied; he had never felt a rope before in his short life.

The powerful creature pulled on the rope with the strength of two horses. The tree creaked and groaned. The canyon echoed and re-echoed with each cry as though a hundred horses were fighting a hundred men. Suddenly, snap went the rope. The stallion reared. He was free. Crazed, he tore over rocks and trees, the piece of frayed rope trailing after him, his band following their leader around and around the walled canyon, trying to find a way out.

Wildhorse now wanted the white leader more than ever. What a strong animal he must be! The horses were trapped but they were not caught. What could he do, with his only rope gone? He sat down on a rock to think. If he let the horses get away now, he would probably never see them again. Box Spring was far from home. It might be that no Indian would come here for several days, unless in search of water as he was. He looked at the restless horses. He must have that beautiful white stallion!

At least one thing he knew. There was water in the canyon. Even though the way was long and rough for a wagon, he would bring his water barrels here and fill them.

It must be past noon. He must be starting back if he would reach his hogan by night—starting back without the white stallion, too.

Wildhorse turned to take away the blanket from the canyon entrance and mount his horse. But as he turned, he saw far off three horsemen riding toward him. They must be searching for water. He waited for them to come up. As the horsemen drew nearer, he saw they were Navajo. They were old friends. Cowboy John, Black Eagle, and Little Singer. They would have ropes. Every Indian carried a rope.

When his friends joined him, Wildhorse told them of the animals that were caught in Box Spring. The four Indians rode up to the entrance, and saw the beautiful horses. Together they laid a plan. Cowboy John and Black Eagle were cattle owners and expert cowboys. They would ride down the stallion.

With a yell, Cowboy John threw his lariat toward the stallion, urging his own horse forward. The rope missed. Black Eagle tried. This time the rope fell over the horse's head. The Indian pulled it tight. His pony stiffened his legs. Black Eagle's pony was wise. He was a trained cowpony. The stallion was caught. Cowboy John ran and tied him up.

The cries of the horses, the yells of the excited Indians, echoed in the once-quiet canyon like the noise of a battlefield. A frightened rabbit ran almost over Wildhorse's moccasin. Birds flew away. A coyote crawled out from behind some rocks, driven from his hiding place by the racket. For an hour Indians chased the horses. Their white leader caught, the other horses did not care what happened to them. In a little while, the Indians had roped all five of them securely.

That evening, four Navajo Indians traveled slowly toward the setting sun. Following the sturdy cowponies, snorting and kicking, danced a string of wild horses. At last they were brought to the corral, never again to roam the high mesa country. In time the horses, now gentle and useful, plowed the land and pulled the wagons.

Wildhorse wanted only the white stallion for his own. The other Indians took the four remaining horses.

Now Dancing Cloud rides a beautiful white horse, the son of the white stallion. And Dancing Cloud's father is called Wildhorse, his nickname, because he caught the wild horses of Box Spring that hot summer which everyone remembers.

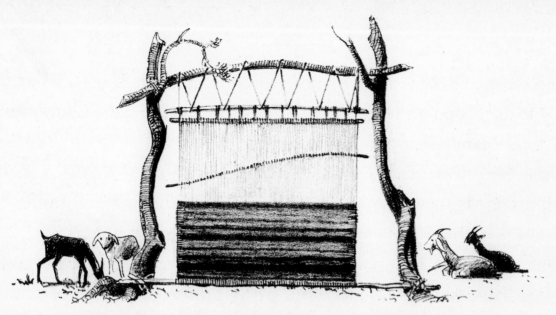

DANCING CLOUD'S MOTHER

YEARS ago, when Dancing Cloud's mother was a little girl, she lived in a hogan at Sweetwater, a few miles to the north of where she now lives. Her mother was a fine weaver and spent much of her time making blankets.

The little girl, at that time, was called Slim Girl. Navajo Indians usually have two names, a sacred or war name, and a nickname. A Navajo's sacred name is not often used. Few of his friends even know what it is, for the Indians believe that the sacred name may wear out if it is used too often.

The nickname changes as its owner grows older. So it is with white people.

Dancing Cloud and Lost Tooth are nicknames. So is Wildhorse a nickname, and Many Goats.

Slim Girl was always happy when her mother began a new rug. What would the new one be like? She would sit behind her mother's loom for hours, watching the pattern grow under the swift fingers.

One day, when her mother had gone to the trading post for coffee and flour, the child sat down before the partly finished rug. The pattern woven there was beautiful to her, a bright red zigzag in a field of black and gray. She thought she could carry out the pattern she had watched her mother weave so often. It looked easy.

For a long time, Slim Girl sat at the loom trying to make the red wool go in and out as she had seen her mother do. The threads became tangled and broken. Sorry she had touched the yarn, she tried to get the pattern right. Far off she heard a galloping horse. She ran to the curtain door and looked out. In the distance she could see her mother on her pony. Quickly she hid the ball of yarn in the box and began to play with her puppies. She tried to forget what harm she had done.

When the mother came in, she laid the sack of flour down on the ground and said to Slim Girl: "What have you been doing all of the time I have been away?"

"Playing with the puppies," answered Slim Girl. Tears were in her eyes. The mother looked at her closely.

"What is the matter?" she asked.

"The smoke," answered the child.

The mother turned toward the loom and a look of surprise came over her face.

"Someone has touched the weaving," she said, and turned quickly to the little girl. "Was anyone here while I was away?" she asked.

"No, Mother."

"Then did you touch the rug?"

"Yes, Mother, I did," and the child burst into tears.

"I want to weave, too, Mother, and I thought I could do it."

"You must not touch the rug again. You are too young. Weaving is hard. First learn to comb out the wool and spin it into thread and when you are eight years old, I will teach you to weave."

"Yes, Mother," answered the child sadly.

The next day Slim Girl went out alone to herd the sheep while the mother mended the weave. She was lonely. She had only a baby brother. All day long she thought about the rug, sorry she had touched it. How she would like to grow up so that she could weave! Water, lightning, and many other designs she had in her mind. When the sheep lay down at noon, she drew patterns in the sand with a stick.

Once she had seen a sand painting on the floor of a Navajo hogan. The Medicine Man had been called to make a sick Navajo well. He and his helpers had made a picture with colored sands on the ground. It was to drive out evil spirits from the sick man.

With colored sands, she could make a picture on the desert floor. Colored sands were all about her. In the creek she found gray and white. She used charcoal from an old fire for black. She piled up four little hills of sand on the ground: red, black, white, and gray. Those were the same colors her mother used. Then she drew her pattern with a stick. She filled in the pattern with different colors of sand. When it was all finished, it looked much like a rug to her. She had found a new game.

In the days that followed, this Navajo child made many pictures on the floor of the desert. Each picture she made was better than the last one. Each noon, when the sheep lay down to rest, she made rugs on the ground. The time seemed to fly.

One day, happy in her game, she did not hear someone step near her. It was the mother. She looked at the child's picture on the desert.

"What is this you are making?" she asked.

"A rug, Mother," said the startled child, "I will make when I am old enough to weave."

"It is beautiful," said the mother. "You want very much to weave, don't you?"

"Yes," said Slim Girl simply.

"You are one of the favored ones," the mother told her. "I will make a small loom for you tomorrow. I will help you put the threads on it. I will show you how to weave."

The child could hardly wait for the sun to go down, so that she could take her sheep home. Tomorrow she would have a loom of her own.

It came about that Slim Girl, when she grew up, became a very fine

weaver. She is now Dancing Cloud's mother, and is called The Weaver. The trader always likes to see her come with a rug tied to her saddle. He knows it will be well made, and easy to sell to the white people who know Navajo rugs.

Now that Dancing Cloud's mother has her own family to care for, she cannot weave as much as she would like to do. She must cook, sew, and do her part of the shearing and herding of their sheep. But when she has any time, this Navajo mother sits down at her loom. She weaves with bright wool yarns the patterns that come to her as she works about her busy hogan. She is an artist.

WATERING DAY AND A RABBIT

SEVERAL years ago, Wildhorse dug a deep hole in the bed of dry Cottonwood Creek, three miles from the hogan. He made a well for watering sheep. He lined the well with stones. Over the top he placed heavy logs, so that no thirsty animal might fall in and drown.

Water slowly seeped up from below the dry creek bed and almost filled the well. The Navajo then hollowed out a log for a trough and placed it near the well. Ever since that day, the two children drive their flock of sheep to this well and dip the water up into the trough. Even in hot summer, the Navajo sheep go for two or three days without water, except what they are able to find in the bits of green plants among the barren rocks.

One hot July morning Dancing Cloud said to Lost Tooth: "Today the sheep need water. I will ride ahead on Long Ears and fill the trough. You follow with the flock."

The boy mounted Long Ears who, in spite of a sharp stick, took his own time in going the three miles. The burro did not like to leave the hogan and go down to the hot sandy creek. When he arrived at the well, Dancing Cloud noticed tracks of horses, cattle, and coyotes in the sand; water was scarcer than usual this summer. But there was plenty of water in Wildhorse's well for the sheep. The heavy logs were able to keep out all uninvited animals.

The boy lay down on the top of the well. He let the old bucket drop into the cool water. Up he pulled it brimming full and poured the water into the trough. He drew another and another. The trough was almost overflowing, when up the creek he heard a great bleating. Lost Tooth and the dogs were driving the sheep. They needed no urging. They were thirsty! They seemed to have wings on their feet.

Dancing Cloud rested and watched the animals. They speeded up as they neared the well. He loved to hear their bleating suddenly die down as they sucked in great gulps of cool water. Soon the sheep were satisfied. Dancing Cloud filled the trough again. The slower, weaker sheep and the young lambs finished what was in it.

The sheep stood around quietly, now. They searched for shade under juniper trees. They settled down in friendly little groups for the noonday rest.

The children knew that the flock would be quiet for several hours. This was their time to play. Lost Tooth had hidden some of her toys—all made of clay—in a little hole. She had made horses, dogs, and a tiny Long Ears.

Dancing Cloud said: "I think I will take my bow and arrow and my greasewood wand for catching rabbits and I will climb Twin Buttes. There I may find something for supper."

"I am tired of mutton," said Lost Tooth. "Go and hunt while I stay here with the sheep."

Twin Buttes was a wild and lonely country. Caves dotted the cliffs. Eagles made nests on rocky ledges. Coyotes made their homes under the rocks.

Dancing Cloud pulled his wide-brimmed hat over his eyes, and took his bow and arrow and his wand for catching rabbits. The wand was a straight greasewood stick soon to be used as all Navajo boys use it when they go out after rabbits. The climb to the top was slow and hot work. His eyes went everywhere. He saw a rattlesnake stretched out on a ledge. He passed it by. Prairie dogs barked at him, and when he threw stones at them they dived into their holes. A horned toad almost ran over his foot. Up in the deep-blue sky soared buzzards. Some dead animal must be lying in the sagebrush on the other side of the buttes.

A small rabbit jumped up from behind a juniper bush and scurried away. The Navajo boy saw it squeeze into a hole between rocks. He was almost as fast as the rabbit. Deep in the hole he could see it, too far back for him to reach with his hand. He took his long stick of greasewood and wet it at one end with his mouth. Then he poked the wand into the hole. When it touched the rabbit, he whirled the stick in his hands. The wet end of the wand buried itself tightly in the fur. Slowly he pulled out the brown, fat, and frightened rabbit.

Tucking the supper rabbit under his arm, he started back down the steep side of the butte on a run. He yelled as he ran and far away he could see the sheep dogs watching him. Like a mountain goat the boy jumped over rocks and bushes. As he neared the well, he tripped over a hidden root and down he fell. The rabbit jumped out of his arms and ran away.

The sheep dogs came running, eager to chase. Dancing Cloud rose to his feet. He took from his bag the bow and arrow. The rabbit had circled and now was coming toward him. The frightened little animal hid himself for a moment under a bush. Dancing Cloud took aim. Whiz went the arrow. Out sprawled the rabbit, just as the boy had sprawled a short time before. This time the supper could not run away. "Look, Little Sister," smiled Dancing Cloud, holding up the limp rabbit for her to see, "now we will have something beside mutton for supper."

PLANTING CORN

ONE May morning, Wildhorse said to Dancing Cloud: "We start to plant corn in the field near the wash this morning. It will soon be warm. The spring and summer rains will come, and the corn will sprout."

"I will help," said Dancing Cloud.

East of the hogan, the father had fenced about a small patch of level ground so that Long Ears, the burro, would not get into the young corn. He had several tin cans full of beautifully marked seed corn saved from last year's crop. Some seeds were pure black. Some grains were white, striped with red. Some were yellow and even orange, some with bright purple lines. This bright-colored corn has been grown by Indians for years. It is very hardy corn which will grow in a country of little rain, of much wind, and under very hot sun. Finer kinds of corn would die in such a fierce climate.

Father and son wound red handkerchiefs around their heads and went down into the field. Wildhorse carried a long pointed stick. Dancing Cloud brought the tin can full of seed corn.

Wildhorse kneeled down on the ground. He thrust his planting stick several inches into the soil. Below the surface the ground was damp and cool. In each hole the boy dropped six or seven kernels and covered them over. Then they went on to the next hole a foot or so away. It took them a long time to plant a small part of the field. The sun was high overhead before all of the corn in the can was gone.

Dancing Cloud asked: "Will we plant beans and squash and melons too?"

"Yes," said the father, "in the other part of the field."

For days in the bright spring weather, the two Indians planted their seeds. A week after the seeds were snugly buried in their beds, great white, billowy clouds appeared in the sky. They poured down torrents of rain. When the brief rain was over, the soil where the seeds lay was soaking in life-giving water.

"Unless cut worms come this year," said Wildhorse, "we should have much corn."

"I hope," said Dancing Cloud, "corn mush and corn cakes."

Dancing Cloud had heard there would be many peaches that year in the canyon de Chelly and near the Hopi villages. The trees were already full of blossoms. The Spanish Fathers had planted those trees a great many years before. The trees still bore fine fruit.

Many times during the month that followed, Wildhorse and his son watched their field carefully. When August rains fell they guided the water to their corn and squash. When sandstorms threatened, they built a windbreak of sagebrush, like a wall of branches to keep the sand away. But even with the windbreak, twice they dug out their corn from sand that had almost buried it.

In late summer they had a fine crop of melons, corn, beans, and squash. Some of it Long Ears, the burro, stole when he broke through the fence. Dancing Cloud did not see him until he had eaten quite a good deal of corn. He chased him out with a big stick, but Long Ears didn't seem to mind at all. He would do it again whenever he could find a weak place in the fence.

THE GREAT CLOUDBURST

DANCING CLOUD'S parents were going to the trading post at White Cone and Dancing Cloud was going with them to buy a new hat. Lost Tooth would take care of the sheep all day.

It was a long trip to the trading post. The family would not return until some time toward evening. The Weaver took the coffee pot along and some cold mutton. The three would eat their noonday meal on the desert.

Lost Tooth drove her flock of sheep toward a favorite grazing place, Cottonwood Creek. She laughed at the young lambs. In the flock were three-months-old lambs. The lambs were happiest in the flocks; they bucked and tumbled over one another like puppies. They had to be watched, for these young and foolish lambs had not learned to stay close to the main flock for safety.

This was August, the month of summer rains, and three times already water had fallen from the skies and had poured in a tiny stream along the sandy creek bottom. There was much grass along the edge of the wash. The sheep fed busily all morning. When the sun was overhead, the flock divided into small groups. Each group found shelter under old juniper trees.

Lost Tooth was tired. She found a shady spot under an overhanging rock along the wash. She lay down to watch her flock. The dogs lay down, too. The air was hot.

For a while the child watched huge white clouds floating overhead. They moved very fast. She could imagine people and animals in them as they changed. Soon her eyelids became heavy. Before she knew it, she was fast asleep, as quiet as the dogs and the sheep.

Overhead, white clouds changed to gray. A hot wind sprang up. In an hour, the sky was almost all gray. The child slept on.

Suddenly thunder like cannon shots echoed across the desert. A stroke of lightning struck a far-off cliff. Lost Tooth awoke with a start. Was it night? The sheep stirred uneasily.

In the north, from a low-lying cloud, poured a gray curtain of water. Lost Tooth had lived all her life on the ever-changing desert. Now when she saw a storm coming she knew what it meant. The Sun God and the Water God were fighting. It was time to get her flock to the corral.

Lost Tooth signaled the three sheep dogs to drive the sheep across the

creek bottom. No water flowed there this day. Even the pools had dried up under the fierce August sun. The girl rounded up the flock, rattling her tin can filled with stones. She drove them across the dry creek bottom and up the steep bank on the side toward Pottery Butte. She would be lucky if she could get them home before the skies poured rain. The dogs felt the oncoming storm and helped well.

The flock was started for home when the Navajo child heard a sad little bleat. She looked back at the spot on the far side of the creek where she had slept. A favorite lamb was calling. He had lost his mother. "Come and get me," he baaed.

Lost Tooth left her flock and ran back again to the other side of the creek. Although the girl could see the pouring rain away up on the horizon no drop of rain had yet fallen at the creek. The bottom of it was as dry as when she had first come with the sheep that morning. Up the other bank she scrambled and picked up the little lamb.

But now from up the creek came a roar like the growling of many mountain lions. Already rushing madly along, a mass of brown foaming water moved down the creek with the swiftness of wild horses. On its foamy crest tumbled stumps of trees, rocks, and logs. A little rabbit tried to swim its current, only to sink out of sight.

This was a cloudburst. She had often heard her father tell how a cloudburst could suddenly fill a dry creek bed with water. A wall of angry, boiling water rushed between her and her sheep. At least, she thought, the dogs on the other side were with the flock. They would guard them.

Carrying her little lamb in her arms, Lost Tooth wandered up and down. She hoped the water would soon go down, so that she could get to her flock on the other side of the angry stream. But it did not. She remembered the old wooden bridge downstream a half a mile.

Blinded by wind, rain, and hailstones the child slowly stumbled to the place where the bridge had been. It was gone. Only broken logs on each side of the creek showed that a bridge had once been there.

During this time, Dancing Cloud and his parents had driven to White Cone. There they met many of their friends. They bought food and started for home. Dancing Cloud was happy over his new hat with the beaded hatband.

They neared a low hill called Coyote Pass. Wildhorse said: "Do you see

the black cloud? That looks like a cloudburst. We must get home."

They urged the horses forward. It was toward evening when the wagon reached Pottery Butte. The rain had caught them.

In the corral were no sheep. In the hogan was no Lost Tooth. The father, mother, and brother started out in their wet clothes to find the girl and the sheep. It was almost dark. Lightning still flashed across the sky and thunder echoed in the hills.

After searching for several miles over the desert, they came upon the flock, which the dogs were still guarding in the dark. The sheep, wet and unhappy, huddled together for warmth. Dancing Cloud and his mother drove them to the corral. Wildhorse wandered searching for the lost child.

The Navajo father knew what harm cloudbursts could do. He knew how a dry creek bed could fill up to the brim with water. And he feared the quicksands. He searched and called for his child. Far into the night he wandered. At Cottonwood Wash the water was beginning to go down. He crossed the stream and looked everywhere. He called and called, but only wind and rain answered him.

At last he gave up hope of finding the child in the black night, and dragged himself sadly homeward. At the curtain door of his hogan, The Weaver sprang up, smiling.

"The child is home," she cried. "She has been here a long time. There she lies, asleep, her lamb in her arms."

On her sheepskin lay Lost Tooth, warm, safe, asleep. The Weaver told Wildhorse how the child had wandered up and down the stream until the water began to go down. Then she had found a shallow place to cross on stones.

The next day, the family learned more of the fury of the storm. An uncle, Crooked Finger, near Rabbit's Ear Mountain, had lost twenty head of sheep. The foolish sheep had looked for shelter from wind and rain in the canyon. The water had rushed down upon them and carried them away.

Another Indian had lost his saddle horse in quicksand which had sucked him down in the bed of the creek. The cloudburst had spread ruin far and wide. Even leaves had been taken from trees. Hailstones as large as walnuts had piled themselves in corners of the rocks. The Navajo family at Pottery Butte was fortunate that Lost Tooth had managed to escape without losing a single animal.

SPRING SHEARING

DANCING CLOUD and his sister looked forward to the week that was starting. Their mother had asked her brother, Many Goats, and his five children to come and help with the shearing, when the wool was cut from the backs of the sheep. Mutton would always be stewing in the black kettle. Perhaps they would have dried peaches and jam to eat. Their uncle would tell them a new story each evening.

Of the shearing of sheep, the carding of wool, and the weaving of rugs, The Weaver always took charge. Most of the sheep were hers. Only a few belonged to Wildhorse. For the Navajo mother in each family owns most of the sheep; the father owns horses and jewelry. When the mother dies, her children get all her sheep. The father receives nothing. If he has any sheep, he has gotten them from his mother. Even the Navajo name for "home" means "My Mother's Place."

The Weaver, then, took full charge of the shearing. She had made wool and rug making the main thing in her life. Long ago, as you know, Dancing Cloud's grandmother had discovered that The Weaver was one of the favored ones, a true artist among weavers.

This June, Dancing Cloud was old enough to help the men and women with shearing. He could tie the legs of the sheep so they would be quiet while they were sheared. He could cut a slit with the shears in an ear of every lamb; he would then know them if they should be lost from the flock. He could keep the shears sharp by grinding them on the grinding stone. Lost Tooth and the three older children of Many Goats could help pile wool against the corral.

Lambs and children played about in dusty wool and tumbled over one another. While the Indians were shearing, one of the old sheep got away from the others, and ran toward the mesa. Dancing Cloud saw her first. He

jumped on his horse and galloped after her. He swung his lasso through the air. To his surprise it fell around the neck of the frightened sheep. The other children laughed as they watched him tugging and pulling. He dragged the runaway back to the shearers. She, too, got her wool all cut off.

By the evening of the fifth day, a great pile of wool lay against the corral, full of dirt, sand, and burrs. The lambs bleated at being taken away from their mothers. The old sheep looked thin and cold after shearing.

Finally no more sheep were left to shear. The men began to pile wool into big gunny sacks. Later it would be hauled to the trading post to exchange for food and clothing. Then it would be sent by truck and train to the White Man's cities to be made into warm clothing.

The Weaver was busy. She picked out black, brown, and white wool for the rugs she planned to weave. It was dirty. She would wash it with soap from roots of the Yucca plant. The Yucca is a Cactus plant that grows in the Southwest. Lost Tooth had already gathered many roots. She pounded them and threw them into the pot of water outside the hogan. The water became milky. The Weaver put in her wools and washed them. Then she hung them out to dry. When dry, they became soft and fluffy.

The Weaver was a good worker and wanted her wool to be clean so that it would take the dye well. But many Indians do not wash wool at all. They know that when it is combed out most of the dirt will fall out. But dirty wool never takes dye as well as wool that is free of dirt and grease.

Firemaker, the wife of Many Goats, helped with carding and spinning. The two women sat down in the shade of the summer house. Firemaker took a handful of newly washed wool. She placed it between her carding tools. The carding tools were two pieces of wood with sharp teeth on the inside, like curry combs. Firemaker scraped the cards back and forth, drawing out the wool until it was light and fluffy. She handed it to her sister to spin.

The Weaver took the carded wool and twisted it with her fingers until she had a long thread. She turned the spindle, winding the thread on it. She worked so fast, Firemaker could hardly keep up with her. The thread on the spindle was loose and thick. The Weaver would spin it again and again, until it was tight and strong.

All morning the carding tools flew and the spindle turned. At noon, five balls of strong yarn lay on the ground, as large as pumpkins. While the women worked and talked, Lost Tooth attended to Firemaker's baby. She

put the sheepskins out to air in the sun. She swept the dirt floor of the hogan. She watched her aunt and mother card and spin, and handed them clean wool.

That evening the two women had enough wool ready for the rug The Weaver was to begin the following day. As the sun went down Many Goats and his family climbed into their wagon and drove home. Their dogs trailed in the dust behind them. Long Ears brayed a noisy good-bye. Wildhorse told the children they would soon see their cousins again. The next week they were to go to their hogan and help Many Goats with his shearing.

The next morning, The Weaver strung up her loom. Four thick sticks were fastened together to form a square. This was the loom frame. It was placed in the shade of the summer house. The Weaver then wound the loom with the up-and-down threads, white wool for warp. It took her some time to string the loom. After that, however, the weaving went quickly. Lost Tooth watched red, black, and white yarns pile into a design. The Weaver had drawn it on the dirt floor of the hogan the night before and had talked it over with Firemaker. But that design was gone; she now carried it in her head.

Long Ears came over to watch the rug, too. He tangled himself in one of the balls of yarn. Lost Tooth spanked him and drove him away. A lamb watched the sleeping baby in its cradleboard. A green lizard crawled up on the baby, and sunned himself.

Four days passed by before the rug was finished. When the Navajo mother took the rug from the loom frame, it was good. The design was strong in blacks and reds, with touches of gray and brown. It would wear a long time. The Weaver had done her work well.

In the old days, the Navajo wove blankets only for their own use. Now they weave rugs which are not worn and are not used on the floor of the hogan. They are made for sale to the trader. On their shoulders, now, the Navajo women wear Pendleton blankets. These are wool blankets, but they are made in factories by white men.

The following day, the Navajo woman tied her finished rug on the saddle of her horse and rode to the trading post. Big Nose, the trader, liked her new rug. He weighed it on the scales. She was paid according to its weight and a little more because it was so well made. He gave her sugar and coffee and oranges for the children. The children liked oranges better than candy. The Weaver tied the food on the saddle and rode home to Pottery Butte.

EAGLES AND TURQUOISE

ONE May morning Dancing Cloud said to his sister: "I will hunt for eagles in Black Cliff today. Will you herd the sheep until I get back?"

"Yes," said his sister. "Father said he needed eagle feathers for the feather dance. He will be glad."

"Swift Boy may go with me. I am going to his hogan to ask him," said Dancing Cloud.

The boy mounted his horse and rode to get Swift Boy, his favorite playmate. The two friends rode across the desert to Black Cliff. Halfway up this cliff Dancing Cloud had often seen an eagle's nest. Swift Boy stood on the ground. Dancing Cloud climbed the cliff from the south side. It was easy climbing. Then he took his rope and tied an old tin can to the end of it. He had brought the can with him from home.

Dancing Cloud lay down on the very edge of the steep cliff and looked over. Far below him he could just see the twigs that stuck out from the eagle's nest. Slowly he let down the rope with the can on the end.

Down, down, slid the rope like a snake. It dangled just outside the nest. With a shout, Dancing Cloud swung it back and forth. The can banged against the rocks. It would have frightened anything. The boys watched carefully, one above, one below. The old eagles were nowhere to be seen. They must be out looking for food.

After a short time, a baby eagle in the nest became scared of the noise. He fluttered to the edge of the nest. He looked around. The noise kept on. Then the little bird lost his balance. Down he fell. He could not fly very well. Half-falling, half-flying down, he went toward Swift Boy, who waited to catch him.

But the bird did not fall all the way to the ground. He caught himself on a shelf of rock that stuck out far above Swift Boy's head. What a surprise this was to the boys!

Dancing Cloud kept on banging his tin can. Before very long the brother of the first eagle came out, too. He also lost his balance. He toppled over.

[69]

Down he fluttered. Swift Boy thought: "At last we have one." But that bird, too, caught himself on the very shelf where his brother hid.

Although Dancing Cloud kept on banging his can against the rocks, no more birds came out. That must be all there were left in the nest. Dancing Cloud climbed down to the ground. "What shall we do now? How can we get up there?" he asked Swift Boy.

For the next hour the two boys tried every foothold in the rock. The sun was low in the sky when at last Dancing Cloud cried: "A trail, a trail!"

The boys dug their toes into every little hole as they climbed up the old trail. Once Dancing Cloud slipped. A shrub gave way in his hands. He slid, but caught himself just in time. Navajo boys are good climbers. At last, quite out of breath, the friends pulled themselves up on the rocky shelf where the birds had hidden themselves.

"Look, a cave," called Dancing Cloud. "The birds must be hiding in the cave." The cave was black and frightening.

"I saw something move behind a rock in the cave," called his friend. "One of the eagles."

"I'm not afraid," answered Dancing Cloud. Although he was very much afraid, he crawled on his hands and knees into the blackness. The young bird tried to get away from him. He grabbed it by the leg and held on. Then he crawled out into the light.

"Tie his legs. I saw the other one a little farther back," he told Swift Boy.

"One eagle is enough," said Swift Boy, afraid.

"I want the other," said Dancing Cloud, and back he crawled again in spite of his fear.

When his eyes became used to the darkness, the boy could just see the other bird. He grabbed it by the wing. It pecked at him with its beak, but he held on tightly and soon brought it out into the light.

"You hold on to this one. Tie his legs. I saw something else in the cave. It was a jar. I am going back."

"No!" cried Swift Boy. "If it is a jar, the Dawn People lived in the cave. The tchindi, the evil spirits, will punish us. Let us climb to the ground."

"But the jar is not even as far back as the eagles were. The tchindi are only in the back of the cave where it is dark," said Dancing Cloud.

The Navajo boy was already in the cave. His heart beat wildly. He grabbed the jar and dragged it to his friend.

The earthen jar seemed full of sand. The boys dug in it with a stick. Under the sand was something white and blue. Turquoise and white shell beads. The jar was full of turquoise. There was no harm in taking them, the boys thought to themselves. The tchindi were not in the jar. So Dancing Cloud and Swift Boy filled their pockets with the turquoise. They thought of belts, rings, and earrings that the lovely blue stones would make.

Suddenly, they were full of fears they did not understand and they hurriedly took the eagles and half-slid, half-fell down the old trail to the ground. They were glad to get on their horses and gallop homeward through the clean air. More than once they looked behind them in fear.

It was past supper time when they got home. Swift Boy took half of the turquoise and one of the eagles. He spurred his horse so he would get to his hogan before it was entirely dark.

Dancing Cloud showed his father the half-grown eagle. Then out of his pockets he brought turquoise and shells.

"Where did you get these?" asked his father. "They are very old. My father had some like them."

"Oh, we found them in the rocks when we looked for eagles," said

Dancing Cloud, afraid to tell his father of the cave of the Dawn People. "Do you think Big Chest, the silversmith, would take part of them and make jewelry for us with the rest? I want a belt with silver disks on it."

"I am sure he will," answered Wildhorse. "We will go over there in the morning." Then he asked: "Did Swift Boy get some, too?"

"Yes. We divided them."

The next day the two Navajos rode to the hogan of Big Chest. He was resting in the sun. They showed him the turquoise. He told them they were very old. No one had found turquoise like that for many years. He was glad to take part of them to pay for the work.

Swift Boy and Dancing Cloud spent many happy days with the silversmith. They blew the bellows for him. They even hammered out some of the Mexican silver for the belts and rings.

Several weeks passed by.

At last the belt was finished. It was very beautiful. It had eight silver disks on it. In the center of each disk lay a rich blue-green turquoise. Dancing Cloud went alone to Big Chest to get it.

"Do you think the tchindi are in these old turquoise?" Dancing Cloud

asked. He was worried because he had never told his father about the cave or the jar.

"Quiet, boy!" warned the silversmith. "To speak evil or to think evil of the jewels will bring evil to them!"

And so Dancing Cloud spoke no more about the cave or the jewels or the tchindi. And his friend, Swift Boy, never spoke about them again, either. Whether it was because the two boys forgot to be afraid of these turquoise, or whether it was because the jewels were now worn on the warm bodies of living people, no one knows, but it happened that no tchindi ever punished the new owners of the ancient stones. The treasures thus became part of the family jewels of Dancing Cloud's family and Swift Boy's family.

TRADING POST

THE WEAVER told the children one June evening, they could go with her to the trading post in the morning. Five sacks of wool lay in the corner of the corral. Wildhorse would herd the sheep.

The children had two bags full of wool from their own sheep. Dancing Cloud had enough to trade with Long Nose, as the Indians called the white trader, for a bright red silk handkerchief he had seen hanging on a nail in the store. Lost Tooth would buy red velvet for a new jacket and six yards of cotton cloth for a new skirt. The children might even have enough wool for candy, oranges, and peaches, too.

Dancing Cloud and Lost Tooth were dressed and ready before their parents were awake. It was ten miles to the trading post. Dancing Cloud caught the horses and harnessed them to the wagon. He tied his own wool on the back of his saddle horse. A little colt that belonged to his mare would tag along behind him all the way. When they were ready to go, Long Ears was locked in the corral for the day. He might steal corn in the hogan if they left him out—or break a fence.

Down the dusty road the old wagon bumpety-bumped over ruts and rocks and along the floor of Cottonwood Creek, which was dry and sandy. Far off the children at last saw the bright green trees which grew at the spring near the store. At noon they arrived.

Long Nose was busy this time of the year. The store was full of Indians. They stood around and leaned against the counter or sat on the floor. It always took them hours to trade. The store was the meeting place for the Indians. Here they learned all the news of the countryside. They talked about the price of wool and sheep; of what the Government might do; and of the place of the next squaw dance.

Behind the post was a stone storehouse. There Long Nose weighed the wool which the Indians brought him. Dancing Cloud gave him his blanket full of wool. It weighed enough for the silk handkerchief he had wanted so long and for candy and fruit besides. For her wool Lost Tooth got red velvet and cotton cloth for the new dress. At the trading post they met Many Goats, who was also trading his wool. The four of them sat down outside the post and had their lunch of cold mutton, coffee, and the can of tomatoes Long Nose opened for them.

Dancing Cloud said: "Uncle, won't you come home with us and stay all night? We want another story." Uncle Many Goats smiled yes at him. After lunch, Long Nose and Many Goats took the big sacks of The Weaver's wool from the wagon. Long Nose paid the Navajo mother many metal coins for her wool. This was not real money but trade money which she could give to the trader whenever she needed food or clothing. To her it was the same as money. The family would have plenty to eat and wear until fall, when the lambs would be ready to sell.

The Weaver spent some of her money. She bought coffee, flour, potatoes, sugar, canned peaches and tomatoes. The wagon was piled high with food. They would have a feast. In mid-afternoon they started for home. Many Goats was with them.

As they neared Pottery Butte, Long Ears brayed a welcome to them. He would be glad to get out of jail. Wildhorse was coming in with the sheep. It was getting dark. They were all tired.

After supper was over, Many Goats lay back on his pile of sheepskins. The children curled at his feet, waiting. When the old folks had finished talking over what they had heard at the trading post, Many Goats would tell them a story from the old, old tales of the Navajo. Dancing Cloud stared into the fire. Lost Tooth's eyes were closed, dreaming of the wonders she had seen at the trading post and of her new dress. Dancing Cloud put his head down on a sheepskin. Before their uncle could even begin his story, both children were fast asleep.